THE
BABAR™
BABY BOOK

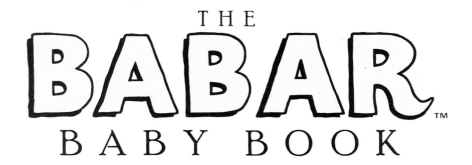

Stewart, Tabori & Chang
NEW YORK

Babar Characters TM & © Laurent de Brunhoff

Published in 1990 by
Stewart, Tabori & Chang, Inc.
575 Broadway, New York, New York 10012

ISBN 1-55670-080-6

Distributed in the U.S. by Workman Publishing,
708 Broadway, New York, New York 10003

This book has been drawn and
art directed by J.C. Suarès.
Design by Joseph Rutt.

Printed in Japan

10 9 8 7 6 5 4 3 2 1

CONTENTS

About Mom 8

About Dad 9

Before Baby 11

Baby is Born 12

Baby Goes Home 16

Baby's Schedule and Behavior 19

Baby's First Bath 21

Religious Services 22

Baby's Names 23

First Visitors 24

Gifts 27

First Outing 29

Baby's Emotions 31

Baby in Motion 34

Baby's Teeth 37

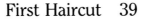

First Haircut   39

Favorite Toys and Games   40

First Foods   44

First Vacation   48

Happy Holidays   51

Baby Talks   57

Baby's First Birthday   60

Baby Walks   65

Baby is Funny   66

Baby's Favorite Stories   68

Baby's Playmates   70

Baby's Caregivers   72

Baby Goes to Playschool   74

Baby's Artwork   76

Baby's Personality   79

ABOUT MOM

Name _____

Birthplace _____

Mom's mother's name _____

Mom's father's name _____

Mom's age at Baby's birth _____

Ethnic and religious background _____

Color of eyes _____ Color of hair _____

Education _____

What was Mom's life like before Baby was born? _____

_____

_____

_____

8

ABOUT DAD

Name _____

Birthplace _____

Dad's mother's name _____

Dad's father's name _____

Dad's age at Baby's birth _____

Ethnic and religious background _____

Color of eyes _____ Color of hair _____

Education _____

What was Dad's life like before Baby was born? _____

_____

_____

_____

BEFORE BABY

Feelings and thoughts about Baby during pregnancy _____

_____

_____

_____

Where was Mom when she went into labor? _____

_____

Where was Dad? _____

How did Mom react? _____

_____

_____

How did Dad react? _____

_____

BABY IS BORN

Baby's name _____

Date of birth _____ Hour _____

Place _____

_____

Name of obstetrician or birth attendant _____

_____

Name of nurse _____

Exact length of pregnancy _____

Duration of labor _____

_____

Kind of delivery _____

_____

Baby's weight _____ Length _____

Circumference of head _____ Chest _____

Apgar score _____

Mom and Dad's first impressions of baby _____

_____

_____

15

Hair and eye color; complexion _____

_____

Family resemblance _____

_____

Behavior _____

_____

BABY GOES HOME

Date _____ Time _____

Mode of transport _____

Weather _____

Names of accompanying friends and relatives _____

_____

16   _____

Observations _____

_____

_____

_____

_____

Description of nursery _____

_____

_____

_____

Name of baby nurse _____

18

Photo

BABY'S SCHEDULE AND BEHAVIOR

Feeding (breast or bottle) _____

_____

_____

Sleeping _____

_____

Crying _____

_____

Names and ages of siblings _____

_____

Their reaction to baby _____

_____

_____

19

BABY'S FIRST BATH

Date _____ Time _____

Place _____

Bathed by _____

Length of bath _____

Bath equipment and toys _____

_____

Baby's reaction _____

_____

_____

Description of event _____

_____

_____

RELIGIOUS SERVICES

Nature of service _____

Baby's age _____

Date _____ Time _____

Place _____

_____

22   Names of guests _____

_____

_____

_____

Baby's behavior _____

_____

BABY'S NAMES

First name ————————————————————

   Significance ————————————————————

Middle name ————————————————————

   Significance ————————————————————

Last name ————————————————————

Baby's nicknames ————————————————————

Photo

FIRST VISITORS

Name _____ Date _____

   Comments about Baby _____

   Baby's reaction _____

Name _____ Date _____

   Comments about Baby _____

   Baby's reaction _____

24

Name _____ Date _____

   Comments about Baby _____

   Baby's reaction _____

Name _____ Date _____

   Comments about Baby _____

   Baby's reaction _____

FIRST VISITORS

Name _____ Date _____

    Comments about Baby _____

    Baby's reaction _____

Name _____ Date _____

    Comments about Baby _____

    Baby's reaction _____

Name _____ Date _____

    Comments about Baby _____

    Baby's reaction _____

Name _____ Date _____

    Comments about Baby _____

    Baby's reaction _____

GIFTS

_____

_____

_____

_____

_____

_____

27

_____

_____

_____

_____

_____

_____

FIRST OUTING

Date _____ Time _____

Where to _____

_____

With whom _____

Weather _____

Baby's outfit _____

Baby's mode of transport _____

Comments from neighbors and passersby _____

_____

_____

Baby's reaction _____

_____

Photo

BABY'S EMOTIONS

Date Baby first smiles _____

Place _____

_____

At whom or what _____

Description of moment _____

_____

31

_____

_____

_____

_____

Date Baby first laughs out loud _____

_____

Imitates facial expressions _____

_____

Understands or makes up a joke _____

_____

_____

_____

Words and phrases that make Baby laugh _____

_____

Baby laughs when _____

_____

Baby enjoys _____

_____

Baby cries when _____

_____

What comforts Baby _____

_____

_____

_____

BABY IN MOTION

Date Baby's eyes first follow a moving object _____

_____

Sucks thumb _____

Holds up head _____

Rolls over _____

Holds and shakes rattle _____

_____

Points at objects _____

_____

Imitates sounds and movements _____

_____

Holds bottle _____

Sits alone _____

_____

Crawls with tummy touching ground _____

_____

Crawls on hands and knees _____

_____

Pulls himself or herself up to standing position _____

_____

Claps _____

Holds spoon _____

Holds cup _____

Baby's special movements _____

BABY'S TEETH

When did Mom and Dad first notice Baby's teething? _____

_____

Baby's reaction to teething _____

What soothes Baby _____

Date bottom front teeth erupt _____

_____

Date upper front teeth erupt _____

_____

Other teeth and dates they erupt _____

_____

_____

_____

FIRST HAIRCUT

Date _____ Time _____

Place _____

Who cut hair? _____

Baby's reaction _____

_____

_____

Lock of Baby's hair:

FAVORITE TOYS AND GAMES

Age _____

    Favorite toy _____

    How Baby plays with toy _____

Age _____

    Favorite toy _____

40   How Baby plays with toy _____

Age _____

    Favorite toy _____

    How Baby plays with toy _____

Age _____

    Favorite toy _____

    How Baby plays with toy _____

FAVORITE TOYS AND GAMES

Favorite games _____

_____

_____

_____

_____

42 _____

_____

Most playful times of the day _____

_____

_____

Favorite security object _____

_____

Other toys _____

_____

_____

_____

_____

43

_____

_____

_____

_____

_____

FIRST FOODS

Date Baby starts solid foods _____

Who fed baby? _____

How much did baby eat? _____

_____

First finger foods _____

Weaned from breast _____

First manages a cup _____

Gives up the bottle _____

First manages a spoon _____

Funny food likes and dislikes _____

_____

_____

FIRST FOODS

Food _____ Date served _____

Baby's reaction _____

Food _____ Date served _____

Baby's reaction _____

Food _____ Date served _____

Baby's reaction _____

Food _____ Date served _____

Baby's reaction _____

Food _____ Date served _____

Baby's reaction _____

Food _____ Date served _____

Baby's reaction _____

Age _____

   Favorite foods _____

   Favorite beverages _____

   Favorite snacks _____

Age _____

   Favorite foods _____

   Favorite beverages _____

   Favorite snacks _____

Age _____

   Favorite foods _____

   Favorite beverages _____

   Favorite snacks _____

FIRST VACATION

Dates _____

Itinerary _____

_____

Mode of travel _____

Traveling companions _____

What Baby brought along _____

What Baby saw _____

_____

Baby's reactions _____

_____

Comments about Baby along the way _____

Notes on trip _____

48

HAPPY HOLIDAYS

Baby's first family holiday _____

Date _____

Place of celebration _____

Baby's outfit _____

Baby's behavior _____

_____

Gifts _____

_____

_____

Guests and their comments about Baby _____

_____

_____

51

OTHER HOLIDAYS

Holiday name _____

Date _____

Place of celebration _____

Baby's outfit _____

Baby's behavior _____

52

_____

Gifts _____

_____

_____

Guests and their comments about Baby _____

_____

_____

Holiday name _____

Date _____

Place of celebration _____

Baby's outfit _____

Baby's behavior _____

_____

53

Gifts _____

_____

_____

Guests and their comments about Baby _____

_____

_____

OTHER HOLIDAYS

Holiday name _____

Date _____

Place of celebration _____

Baby's outfit _____

Baby's behavior _____

_____

54

Gifts _____

_____

_____

Guests and their comments about Baby _____

_____

_____

Photos

BABY TALKS

Date Baby coos in response to Mom or Dad _____

_____

Babbles _____

_____

Makes word sounds _____

_____

Baby's first word _____

_____

Says "Mama" _____

Says "Dada" _____

Baby's unique words _____

_____

Baby's names for family and friends _____

_____

_____

_____

Baby's first two-word combination _____

_____

_____

Longer phrases _____

_____

_____

Baby's way of greeting _____

_____

Baby's first story _____

_____

_____

First song _____

_____

_____

Funny things Baby says _____

_____

_____

_____

_____

BABY'S FIRST BIRTHDAY

Time _____

Place _____

Events of the day _____

_____

_____

60

_____

Baby's outfit _____

_____

Menu _____

_____

Baby's reaction to cake _____

_____

Guests at Baby's first birthday party _____

_____

_____

_____

_____

62

_____

Gifts received _____

_____

_____

_____

_____

Photos

BABY WALKS

Date Baby stands holding on _____

Walks with help _____

Takes first steps alone _____

    Where _____

    To whom _____

Baby's reaction _____

_____

Mom and Dad's reaction _____

_____

Notes about walking _____

_____

_____

65

BABY IS FUNNY

Stories about Baby _____

_____

_____

_____

_____

_____

_____

_____

_____

More stories about Baby _____

_____

_____

_____

_____

_____

_____

_____

_____

BABY'S FAVORITE STORIES

Baby's favorite storyteller _____

Favorite stories _____

_____

Favorite reader _____

Favorite books _____

_____

_____

_____

Where Baby likes to read _____

What Baby does when read to _____

_____

Date Baby "reads" (names objects in book) _____

BABY'S PLAYMATES

Baby's friends are _____

_____

_____

_____

_____

70 _____

_____

Games they play _____

_____

_____

_____

_____

_____

BABY'S CAREGIVERS

Name _____ Age _____

Term of employment _____

Comments _____

Name _____ Age _____

Term of employment _____

72 Comments _____

Name _____ Age _____

Term of employment _____

Comments _____

Name _____ Age _____

Term of employment _____

Comments _____

BABY GOES TO PLAYSCHOOL

Date _____

Baby's age _____

Name of school or program _____

Description of school or program _____

Name of teacher(s) _____

Baby's reactions _____

_____

_____

Mom and Dad's reactions _____

Baby's favorite activities _____

Names of classmates _____

_____

BABY'S ARTWORK

76

BABY'S ARTWORK

BABY'S PERSONALITY

Birth to six months _____

_____

Likes _____

Dislikes _____

Six months to one year _____

_____

79

Likes _____

Dislikes _____

Fears _____

Displays of affection _____

Displays of curiosity _____

Displays of excitement _____

BABY'S PERSONALITY

One to two years _____

_____

Likes _____

Dislikes _____

Fears _____

Displays of affection _____

Displays of curiosity _____

Displays of excitement _____

Notes on Baby's personality _____

_____

_____

_____